ALL THIS AND SNOOPY, TOO

Selected Cartoons from
YOU CAN'T WIN, CHARLIE BROWN
VOL 1

By CHARLES M. SCHULZ

A FAWCETT CREST BOOK
Fawcett Publications, Inc., Greenwich, Conn.

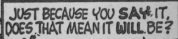

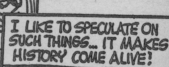

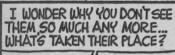

IT ALWAYS SEEMS SO QUIET AROUND HERE ON THE DAY HE GOES TO VISIT HIS GRANDFATHER...

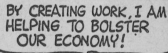

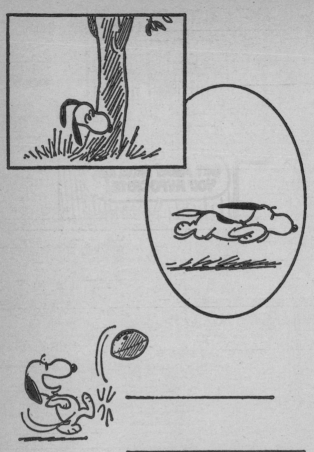

ALL OF EARTH'S CREATURES HAVE, HIDDEN WITHIN THEIR BEINGS, A WILD UNCONTROLLABLE URGE TO PUNT!

OBVIOUSLY, IT IS WAY PAST SOMEBODY'S SUPPERTIME!

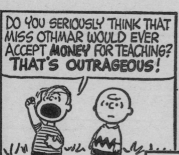

OH, MISS OTHMAR, HOW COULD YOU?

I THOUGHT YOU WERE TEACHING US BECAUSE YOU **LOVED** US! I NEVER DREAMED YOU WERE GETTING **PAID** FOR IT!

WAIT A MINUTE! MAYBE SHE'S GETTING PAID, BUT YET NOT REALLY **ACCEPTING** THE MONEY!

I'LL BET THAT'S IT! I'LL BET SHE'S TURNING IT ALL BACK IN! OH, MISS OTHMAR, YOU'RE A TRUE GEM!!

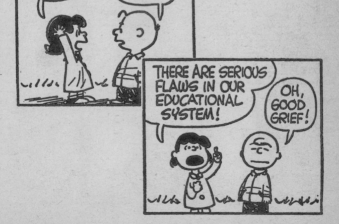

GOOD GRIEF! HERE COMES LUCY! I'M TRAPPED!

SHE SAID SHE'D THROW MY BLANKET IN THE TRASH BURNER THE NEXT TIME SHE SAW IT...

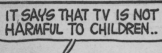

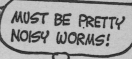

YOU CAN'T HEAR
WORMS THIS TIME OF
YEAR...THE GROUND
IS TOO HARD..

I DIDN'T
REALIZE
"WORM-LISTENING"
WAS SO
SEASONAL!

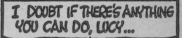

I PROMISED CHARLIE BROWN THAT I'D TRY TO TALK TO YOU, SCHROEDER..

NOW, LET'S BE PRACTICAL ABOUT THIS THING..WHO MAKES THE MOST MONEY, A CONCERT PIANIST OR A BASEBALL CATCHER?

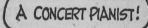

A CONCERT PIANIST!

WHAT'S THE MATTER WITH YOU, CHARLIE BROWN? WHY DON'T YOU LEAVE SCHROEDER ALONE?!